THE Wild Animal WORKBOOK

Designed, written, and illustrated by Hilton Snowdon

This book is lovingly dedicated to Joseph Snowdon and the kids of All Children's Hospital in St. Petersburg, Florida.

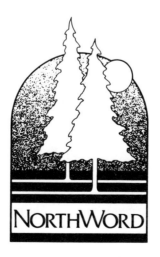

NorthWord

© 1992 Hilton Snowdon

BLUE WHALE

How Long? Up to 100 feet
How Heavy? Up to 392,000 pounds

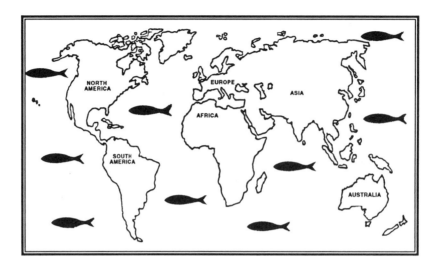

The largest living animal on earth is the blue whale, and females are slightly bigger than males. A blue whale's mouth is 20 feet long! The whale has 10-foot flippers, and its tail flukes are 15 feet across. Believe it or not, the blue whale's heart is the size of a small car. The heart pumps over 10 tons of blood through arteries big enough for an adult person to crawl into. Most people wouldn't want to try it, though.

Oddly enough, the world's biggest animal eats tiny krill shrimp barely two inches long. The blue whale's stomach holds over two tons of krill, and the whale eats a bellyful every single day.

Blue whale mothers give birth to babies that are 23 feet long when they're born, and the thirsty babies drink up to 100 gallons of whale milk a day. A baby whale can gain 200 pounds in just one day.

The blue whale lives in all of our seas and oceans. It may travel alone or in pairs, but it moves in herds when the whales discover a feeding area that's filled with delicious whale food. The whale can dive as deep as 350 feet underwater, and it can stay down for as long as 50 minutes. Imagine trying to hold your breath for almost an hour!

Sometimes blue whales are hunted by packs of killer whales, but an animal this big is good at defending itself. Blue whales often live for 60 years or more.

BLUE WHALE BAFFLERS

- How long can a blue whale hold its breath?
- How big of a baby bottle would a baby blue whale need?
- Is a ten-year-old blue whale very old?
- The big blue whale has a big appetite. What does it like to eat?
- Would you like to crawl inside of a blue whale? Why or why not?

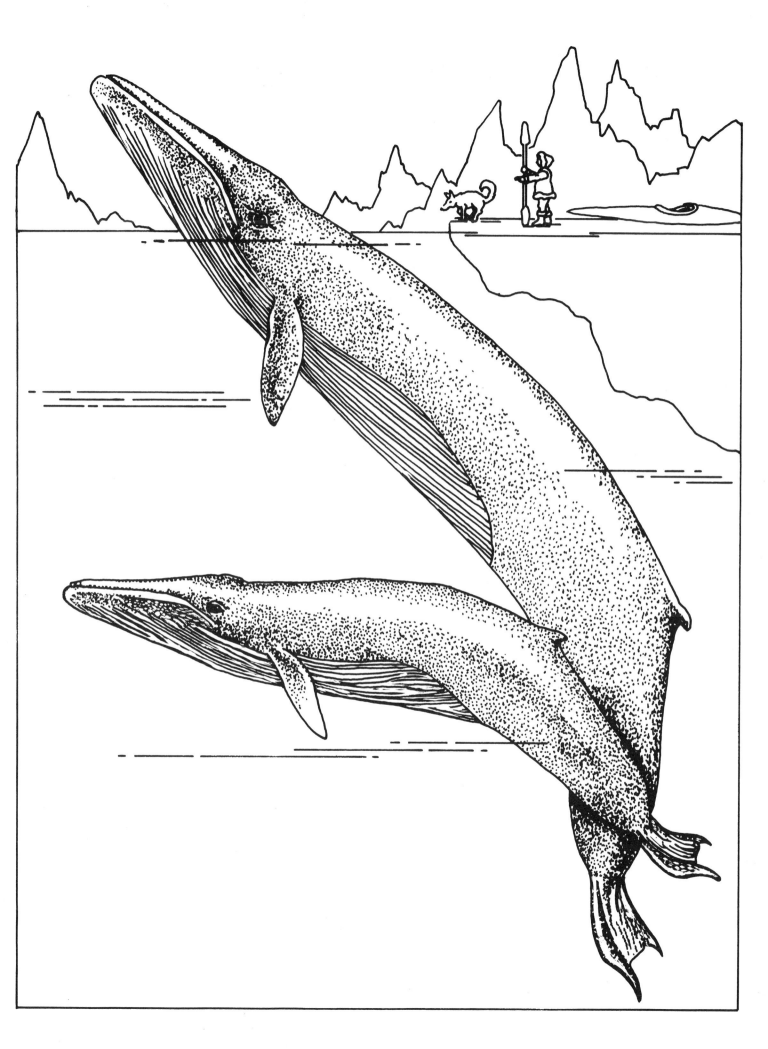

BOTTLENOSE DOLPHIN

How Long? Up to 8 feet, 3 inches
How Heavy? Up to 1,450 pounds

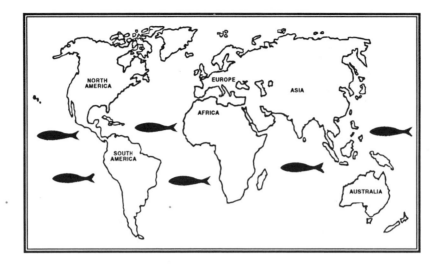

Even though they look fishy, dolphins are not fish. Instead, they're warm-blooded animals found in the warm waters of the world. Off the coast of Florida, they bunch together in herds of 40 or so. The animals then separate into smaller groups called "pods." One pod contains about a dozen dolphins. In other areas, huge "schools" have been spotted that include as many as 300,000 dolphins!

Dolphins have an unusual body condition called "fusion of the neck vertebrae." You could say they have a stiff neck that limits their head movements. But the stiffness helps keep their body shape perfect for high-speed swimming.

Dolphins can't see too well, but their hearing is excellent. They use their voices to send out sounds, and they find their way around by listening to the echoes. Scientists call this way of navigating "echolocation."

The bottlenose dolphin can live to be 35 years old or even older. Dolphin babies are 35 to 50 inches long when they're born, and they'll nurse milk from their mother for about a year before they start to eat solid food. Mothers bear their young every two or three years, and they may have as many as eight babies in their lifetimes. Adult dolphins will actually "baby-sit" an infant for a female while she is busy feeding.

In the past, many dolphins got caught in tuna fishing nets and drowned. But stricter laws and fishing guidelines now help protect these playful, intelligent animals.

DOLPHIN DOOZIES

- What is echolocation?
- Do dolphins have to do homework when they're in a school?
- What human activity has endangered the lives of dolphins?
- What body condition helps the dolphin become a speedy swimmer?
- Would you like to baby-sit a young dolphin? Why or why not?

CHIMPANZEE

Male: How Tall? 31 to 37 inches
          How Heavy? 140 to 170 pounds

Female: How Tall? 28 to 34 inches
            How Heavy? 85 to 100 pounds

The most intelligent animal next to humans is the chimpanzee. Chimps are mischievous, playful, and inventive. They use things they find in nature as tools. For example, a chimp might dip a small twig into a termite hill to get a mouthful of tasty bugs. Or it might sponge up drinking water with a handful of lightly chewed leaves from a hollow tree.

Chimpanzees live in bands of 30 to 80 members, mostly made up of mothers and their young. The larger males roam around, so the band's leadership changes constantly. Chimps make a new sleeping nest out of leaves and twigs every night. They eat fruit, bird's eggs, insects, and small mammals. Sometimes they band together to hunt for young antelopes or even baboons.

Chimpanzees are not really monkeys. They're members of the ape family. Monkeys have long, lean bodies, with their heart, lungs, and stomach located in the same place as animals that walk on all fours. Apes have large chests, and they sit and stand upright. When they're threatened, monkeys bark loudly and show their dog-like teeth, but apes scream and pound their powerful fists downward. So do chimps.

CHIMP CHALLENGES   ?

- What would you find in a chimpanzee's toolbox?
- How would you make a chimpanzee's bed?
- What do chimps eat?
- Is the chimpanzee really just a smart monkey?
- Are you more like a monkey or an ape? What makes you think so?

ELEPHANT

Asiatic Elephant:
How Tall? 8 to 8-1/2 feet
How Heavy? Up to 11,025 pounds

African Elephant:
How Tall? 10 to 13 feet
How Heavy? Up to 13,230 pounds

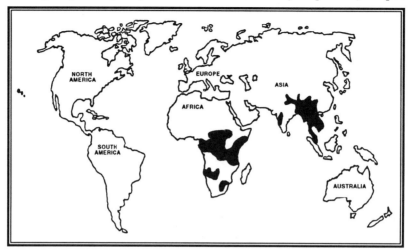

Elephants are the largest land animal. They once lived almost everywhere in the world except Australia. Today, though, herds live in places that are desert-like, in forests, in open woodlands, and on grassy plains. Mostly, that means they live in Africa and Asia.

Elephants aren't picky eaters. They eat grasses, roots, leaves, twigs, bark, nuts, and even the fruit from palm trees. A large bull elephant eats several hundred pounds of food a day. Unfortunately, when elephants feed, they push over whole trees just to eat a few leaves. Or they eat the bark off of big trees, which makes the trees die. They don't mean to do any damage, but it may take the land a long time to recover from an elephant feast.

Elephants drink a lot, too, and they're clever when it comes to finding water in dried-up creek beds. They use their huge tusks, which can be as long as 11-1/2 feet and can weigh over 200 pounds. They dig deeply into the mud with the tusks to reach water. A big female elephant, called a cow, might drink 35 to 50 gallons of water a day.

An elephant's trunk is really its nose. By using its trunk and a finger-like nub at the end of the trunk, the elephant can do amazing things. It can gather food, scratch an itch, spank its young calves, suck up water for drinking, give itself a shower, dust itself off to get rid of insects, and make sounds like a trumpet. You probably never knew a long nose could be so handy.

ELEPHANT EXERCISES ?

- What's a grown-up male elephant called? A grown-up female?
- What do elephants use their tusks for?
- How might an elephant give itself a shower?
- Name one place where elephants have never lived.
- Would you like to be around when an elephant sneezed? Why or why not?

GIRAFFE

How Tall? From 11-1/2 feet to 17 feet, 5 inches
How Heavy? Up to 4,256 pounds

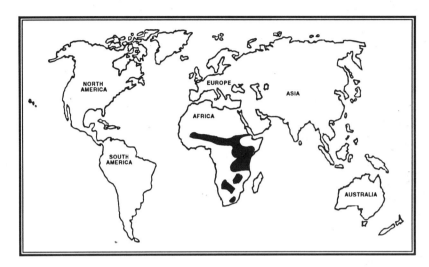

The giraffe is the tallest living mammal in the world. The tallest giraffe ever measured stood over 19 feet high! Much of its height is taken up by its long, long neck. A giraffe has the same number of neck bones as a human (seven), but the giraffe's bones are more elongated.

Giraffes are herbivores, which means they eat plants. They munch on leaves and twigs that they find in treetops. If you look closely, you find out that a giraffe has an unusual mouth. The upper lip extends downward, well beyond the lower lip. It helps them grab branches. Meanwhile, the giraffe's tongue might be as long as 18 inches, and it carries tender leaves into a mouth that has no front teeth!

Sometimes giraffes lie down to sleep, but mostly they sleep standing up. They're less vulnerable to lion attacks when they're standing. Giraffes protect themselves by kicking in all four directions with hooves up to 12 inches wide. When they need to, giraffes can run away from an enemy, reaching speeds of up to 32 miles per hour.

Giraffes band together in herds of as many as 20, but mostly females and their young live in the herds. Male giraffes, known as bulls, are solitary. When they fight over females during the mating season, the bulls swing their long necks and hammer away at each other with their heads. Most of these battles end when both giraffes get too tired to fight any longer.

Giraffes have a short life span of just 15 to 20 years. A female, called a cow, usually bears one calf at a time, but sometimes she has twins.

GIRAFFE GRAPPLERS

?

- How do giraffes defend themselves?
- Would a giraffe eat a hamburger? How do you know?
- Why do giraffes often sleep standing up?
- Describe what happens when two male giraffes are fighting.
- Would you like to have a mouth with no front teeth? Why or why not?

GORILLA

How Tall? Up to 69 inches
How Heavy? 331 to 606 pounds

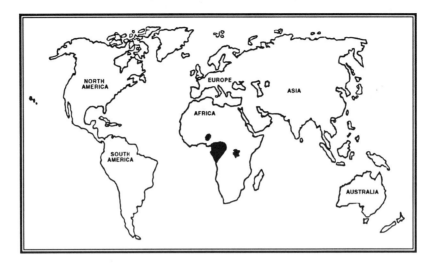

The gorilla is the largest living animal that walks on two feet. It inhabits bamboo and mountain rain forests at high altitudes up to 11,500 feet.

In 1985 there were only three gorilla populations surviving: the Western Lowland group of 14,250 animals, the Eastern Lowland group of less than 5,000, and the most endangered of all—400 mountain gorillas. Sadly, the great ape is near extinction due to logging of the rain forests and illegal hunting.

The gorilla has a strictly vegetarian diet. It eats only plants. It likes to feed on herbs, buds, tender shoots, and stems. Male gorillas are larger than females, and the adult males are called "silverbacks" because of the distinguished color of their hair. Silverbacks beat their chests to keep intruders away, or to find out the location of another gorilla band. The leader of the other band will respond in the same way.

Family groups of 14 to 20 members are led by a dominant silverback. He decides almost everything for the rest of the band: When to get up in the morning, where and when to eat, and where to build nests at night. Gorillas build new nests of leaves, branches, and twigs each night. The large males sleep on the ground, but the females and infants sleep in the treetops.

GORILLA GRILLERS

?

- Why do silverbacks beat their chests?
- Why is the gorilla an endangered animal?
- Would a gorilla prefer hot dogs or bananas for lunch?
- Where do gorillas sleep?
- Would you like to take orders from a big male gorilla? Why or why not?

HIPPOPOTAMUS

How Tall? Up to 5 feet, 5 inches at the shoulders
How Heavy? Up to 9,920 pounds

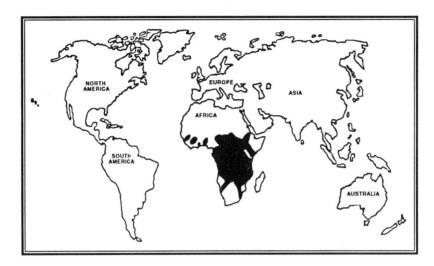

The hippopotamus gets its name from a Greek word that means "river horse." To escape the hot African sun, hippos spend their days underwater for three or four minutes at a time between breaths. Their skin is sensitive to sunburn, and it will blister if it's exposed to the sun for very long. In fact, female hippos raise their young in shallow water.

Hippos may nibble on reeds and water plants during the day, but their real feeding happens at night. They may travel miles searching for the tender plants they like. A full-grown adult can eat 200 pounds of grass and leaves in a single meal.

With their short, stubby legs and their big bellies, hippos look fat and sluggish. But actually, a hippopotamus is all muscle. On land it can outrun a human, and in water it's a strong swimmer.

Hippos have large, razor-sharp tusks about two feet long, which they use for eating. If threatened, they will open their huge jaws, displaying their tusks as a warning to their enemies. Male hippos sometimes fight, and they may seriously hurt each other by biting.

White "cow" egrets are often seen riding on the backs of hippos. They're not riding for fun, though. The birds eat pesky insects that land on the hippo's back. Egrets also follow hippos around, so they can eat fresh worms and other foods they find in the hippos' deep footprints.

HIPPO HEAD-SCRATCHERS ?

- Why do hippos feed mostly at night?
- If you made a salad for a hippo, how big would it have to be?
- What does "hippopotamus" mean in Greek?
- Why do egrets like to hang around with hippos?
- Would you like to have tusks? Why or why not?

KILLER WHALE

Males: How Long? Up to 31 feet, 6 inches
        How Heavy? Up to 18,000 pounds

Females: How Long? Up to 27 feet
          How Heavy? Up to 9,000 pounds

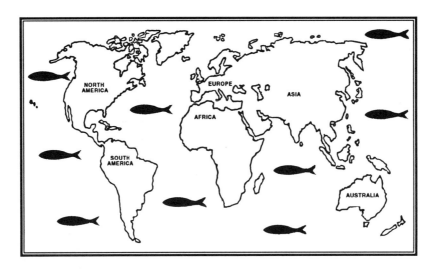

Killer whales are not exactly whales. They're classified as dolphins, and they're the largest members of that family. As the name "killer" suggests, they were once thought of as ferocious hunters. But now we know that, like dolphins, killer whales are intelligent and gentle creatures.

Killer whales prefer cool waters, but they live in oceans from the chilly polar icecap regions to the warm tropics. They travel in herds of 25 to 30 animals, then break off into smaller groups of just two or three. Killer whale families stay together for many years, and they keep in touch with each other by making underwater sounds called vocalizations. Killer whales are full of energy, and people often see them jumping out of the water. They breathe every 10 to 30 seconds, but they can dive underwater for as long as four minutes.

Hunting in packs, killer whales look for fish, dolphins, porpoises, and even other whales. They also hunt for seals, sea lions, and seabirds including penguins. The older male killer whales watch the shore for danger when others are hunting in shallow waters.

A newborn calf is about eight feet long. Each one weighs over 400 pounds, and at first it's a yellowish-pink color in the areas that later turn white. The calf nurses milk from its mother for almost a year.

KILLER QUESTIONS

- Is the killer whale really a whale?
- What do baby killer whales eat for the first year?
- How do killer whales talk to each other?
- How long would an aquarium have to be to hold a full-grown male killer whale?
- Would you be afraid if you met a killer whale? Why or why not?

LION

How Long? Up to 6-1/2 feet
How Heavy? Up to 551 pounds

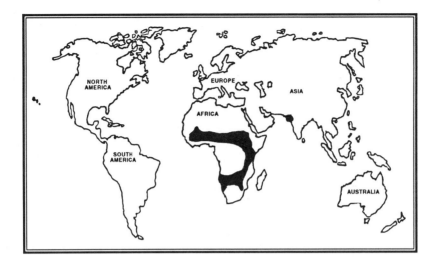

Lions are smart animals. They're successful hunters because they hunt in groups, which allows them to catch animals that are bigger and faster than they are. Lions aren't the fastest of the big cats, but they can run at speeds of up to 35 miles per hour.

A group of lions is called a pride, and a lion pride may include as many as 40 animals. Male lions mark their territory by roaring ferociously and spraying urine on the ground. Lions don't often fight, but a male will chase an intruder for many miles.

Lions eat almost anything, including dead animals. However, they prefer live prey like wildebeest, zebras, impalas, warthogs, and even giraffes. It's unusual for a lion to attack a human, but if the lion is old, sick, injured, or living in an area where man has killed off its natural prey, the lion may turn into a man-eater. A large male may devour 75 pounds of animal meat and skin in a day, but then it will stop eating for several days. A well-fed lion sleeps for as long as 20 hours at a time. That's a long cat nap!

A lioness normally has a litter of two to four cubs, although sometimes up to six cubs are born at a time. Many die, though, because of diseases, accidents, or starvation.

Lions once roamed a vast range, but they now live only in the southern part of the Sahara Desert and in India's Gir Forest. In the 1950s, there were 400,000 lions in the world. Today, there are less than 200,000. Much of the jungle where they lived has become farmland. When land becomes unsuitable for an animal to live in, we call this "habitat loss." Habitat loss is the biggest reason that lion populations have declined.

LION LINGO

- What is a female lion called?
- Name three animals that lions might hunt.
- How does a male lion let others know where its territory is?
- Why are there fewer lions now than there were 40 years ago?
- If it was dinner time for your pet lion, how many one-pound cans of food might you have to feed it?

MORAY EEL

How Long? 8 to 10 feet
How Heavy? 56 to 100 pounds

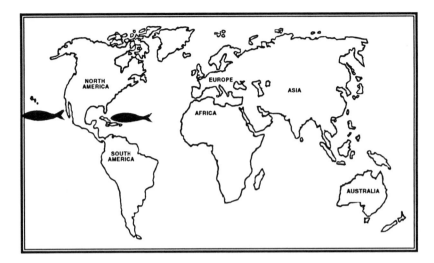

The giant moray eel looks like a big fat snake, but it's really a bony fish. Morays are usually green, and sometimes they have spots.

Female morays are much larger than males, and they'll dive as deep as 3,000 feet underwater so they can lay their eggs on the ocean floor. Each egg hatches into a tiny larva that at first looks like a small, transparent tree leaf. It never grows into a tree, though.

Morays are fierce hunters that coil up in the crevices between rocks and ambush their prey (mostly fish) with needle-sharp teeth. Sometimes they eat so much that they can't squeeze back into their dens. When this happens, they will actually tie themselves in a knot and force the food back out of their mouths, so that they're able to wiggle back into their hide-outs.

Although the moray eel has a reputation for being vicious, it allows little butterfly fishes to swim in and out of its huge jaws unharmed, so that the fishes can eat parasites they find on the eel's teeth.

MORAY MYSTERIES

- Where might you find the eggs of a moray eel?
- How does a moray eel have its teeth cleaned?
- Is the moray a fish or an underwater snake?
- What does a moray larva look like?
- If you were a moray eel, how would you get rid of a stomach ache you got from eating too many fish sticks?

ORANGUTAN

How Tall? Three to five feet
How Heavy? Up to 220 pounds

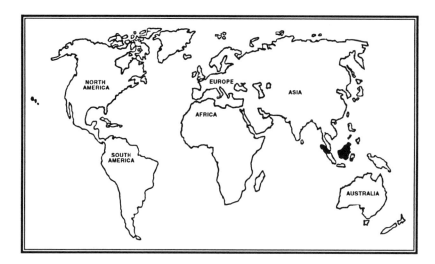

Orangutan means "man of the forest," and orangutans really do look a little like people. But they're actually gentle apes.

Orangutans live in the rain forests of Indonesia. Since the 1980s, many of the trees in those forests have been chopped down, so there are fewer places where the orangutan can survive. Because of this habitat loss, there are now less than 5,000 orangutans in the whole world. It's an endangered species.

The male orangutan is much larger than the female, and the animal's unusual orange color gets darker as it gets older. Orangutans spend most of their lives in treetops, where they eat fruits, leaves, and insects. They climb or swing from branch to branch by using their long arms. When they do travel on the ground, they walk on the outside edges of their feet.

Each night orangutans make a fresh bed of leaves and twigs. In the summer season of heavy rains, called the monsoon, they grab large leaves and use the leaves like umbrellas to help them stay dry!

Adult males grow large cheek and throat pouches. The pouches make their calls resonate, so they can be heard up to a mile away. Female orangutans are about half the size of males. A young orangutan stays with its mother until it's five or six years old. Then it takes off and spends the rest of its life climbing, swinging, and eating in the treetops.

ORANGUTAN RIDDLES

- How do you say "man of the forest" in Indonesian?
- What does an orangutan do with large leaves?
- How does an orangutan's color change as it gets older?
- Describe the way an orangutan walks when it travels on the ground.
- Would an orangutan take good care of your bug collection? Why or why not?

PARROTS

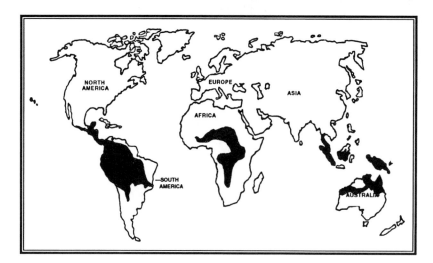

Three hundred and fifteen different birds are part of the parrot group. The birds range from the Papua New Guinea pygmy parrot, which is just over three inches long, to the 40-inch macaw of the Amazon Jungle.

Most parrots have things in common. They have large heads (for the size of their bodies) and short necks. They have hooked bills that curve downward, used for cracking nuts and digging into tough shells. They have strong, grasping feet with a pair of toes in front and a pair in back. They use their feet like hands to help feed themselves.

Parrots live for a long time, sometimes 50 to 80 years. Most parrots travel in flocks and live in treetops, feeding on fruits. Often, though, they invade fields of grain looking for more food.

When they're in the wild, parrots only shriek and squawk. But when they're captured and put in zoos or raised as pets, they learn to imitate many sounds—especially the human voice. The large African gray parrots and the green Amazons are the most skilled at mimicking sounds.

There are some peculiar parrots. The tiny green parakeets that live in India and the Philippines have developed a strange habit. Like bats, they sleep while hanging upside down from their perches. But the strangest of all is the kakapo or owl parrot of New Zealand. During the day, this bird hides in holes in the rocks or under tree roots. It only comes out at night, and it can hardly fly. When it comes out, it quickly climbs trees for fruit and nectar, then glides down to the ground and runs back to its hiding place.

The giant black cockatoo of New Guinea has solid black feathers, while all other cockatoos are white. It has bare skin patches around its cheeks that change from pink to fire-engine red depending upon its mood. If you see a giant cockatoo with red cheeks, you'll know it's upset about something.

PARROT PERPLEXERS

?

- How do the tiny green parakeets of India like to sleep?
- What does it mean to say that parrots are good at mimicking sounds?
- If all the relatives showed up, how many different birds would attend a parrot's family reunion?
- Name some features that almost all parrots have in common.
- Do your cheeks change color according to what mood you're in?

PELICAN

White Pelican:
How Tall? Up to 65 inches
How Wide? Wingspan of up to 9 feet

Brown Pelican:
How Tall? Up to 50 inches
How Wide? Wingspan of up to 6 1/2 feet

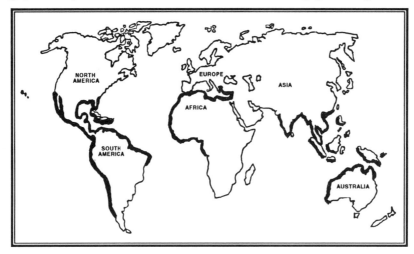

Two species of pelicans make the coastlines around the world their home. The larger of the two is the white pelican, and the smaller is called the brown pelican. Both are considered ancient birds, because scientists have found fossils proving that birds almost identical to pelicans lived 30 million years ago! A pelican alive today may live for more than 30 years.

Birds the size of pelicans need to eat large quantities of food. A full-grown adult will consume about four pounds of food daily. White pelicans hunt together by beating the water with their wings and feet, driving fish into shallow water where the pelicans can scoop them into their pouches. Brown pelicans fish differently. They cruise 10 to 30 feet above the water. When they see a fish, they plunge into the water with half-spread wings. They pop back to the water's surface tail-first, draining the water from their pouches. Then, finally, they swallow any fish they've managed to catch. Sometimes, though, they come up fishless.

Pelicans have a hard time getting airborne, especially when there is no wind to help them. They often run awkwardly on top of the water, flapping their wings desperately. Once they take off, they normally fly either 50 to 100 feet above the water or skim along the surface of the waves. Updrafts of wind lift them just enough so they can glide with only an occasional flap of their wings.

In the air, pelicans look a little like a marching band. They either fly in a straight line or in a "V" formation. Their wing strokes are synchronized, and when they're resting on land or water, they all face the same direction.

PELICAN PUZZLERS

- Which is larger, the brown pelican or the white pelican?
- Describe the way that a brown pelican goes fishing.
- Why do pelicans go jogging on the surface of the water?
- Why do we think of pelicans as ancient birds?
- Would you rather be a white pelican or a brown pelican? Why?

RHINOCEROS

Black Rhinoceros:
How Tall? 4-1/2 to 5-1/2 feet at the shoulders
How Heavy? 2,000 to 4,000 pounds

White Rhinoceros:
How Tall? 5 to 6 feet at the shoulders
How Heavy? 5,000 to 7,000 pounds

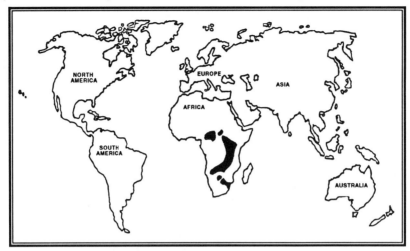

The rhinoceros is one of Africa's plant-eating giants. There are black rhinos and white rhinos in Africa, but both species are now very rare because of illegal hunting. Only about 3,600 white rhinos were alive there in 1984, and the black rhinos number about 9,000. Paintings found on cave walls in many parts of the world tell us that the white rhino was once widespread and plentiful. But rhinos have been hunted for their horns, which were believed to hold magical or healing powers. Actually, the horns are just masses of hard, hair-like fibers.

The white rhinoceros is slow-moving and mild-mannered. It has a large, squared-off upper lip that it uses for grazing, and its two horns can grow up to five feet long. The black rhinoceros is much smaller. It has a pointed lip, its front horn is about four feet long, and it's notorious for its bad temper. Stories about "angry" black rhinos charging cars and people are common, but the rhino probably charges because it has bad eyesight and is afraid when people get too close. Rhinos are especially dangerous when they're with their young. They have even killed lions that came too close.

The rhinoceros easily adjusts to different areas and climates. It lives all across Africa, from the coastal plains through bush country and up in the steep mountain forests. Rhinos can stand intense heat while they graze on grasses and juicy plants called succulents. Each animal needs several square miles of pasture to supply its food needs.

RHINO REMINDERS

- Why might a black rhino attack a person or a car?
- Name two ways in which black rhinos and white rhinos are different.
- How do we know that rhinos once lived in many parts of the world?
- Why have rhinos been illegally hunted?
- How big would your yard have to be to keep a rhino from getting hungry?

TIGER

How Tall? Up to 43 inches at the shoulders
How Heavy? Up to 661 pounds

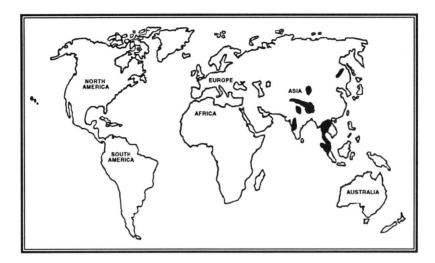

The largest of all the big cats is the tiger. A large tiger species lives in Siberia, but a smaller species can be found as far south as the jungles of Bali. Tigers live in many different habitats, including tropical rain forests, swamps, grasslands, and rocky, desert-like regions.

When it waits under an acacia tree amidst the tall grass, the tiger is camouflaged so well that it's almost invisible. Tigers are hunters that stalk large animals (including people) at night. A tiger can devour up to one-fifth of its weight in a single meal. Tigers live for up to 30 years, and they're incredibly strong. An adult can jump 18 feet into the air, or leap 40 feet across gorges.

In 1965, a study of 50 known man-eating tigers revealed a surprising fact. Forty of the tigers had previously been wounded by bullets, so humans had become the easiest prey for the tigers to catch. This means a tiger wounded by a human may become more dangerous to humans! Over the years, tiger populations have declined because hunters sell their exotic skins illegally.

A female tiger, called a tigress, may bear one to six cubs. She moves the cubs shortly after birth in order to protect them from aggressive male tigers. The males may try to kill the offspring.

Tigers make many noises. They moan loudly to express unhappiness. They roar to warn rivals that they are approaching, or to herd weaker animals into a trap. They bark when they're calling to another tiger, cough to frighten other animals away from a kill, and hiss to blow insects away from a carcass.

TIGER TEASERS

?

- When does a tiger bark?
- Why does a tigress move her babies shortly after they're born?
- Why has the tiger population been shrinking?
- How high can a tiger jump? How far can it jump?
- How many tiger noises can you make?

ZEBRA

How Tall? Up to 59 inches at the shoulders
How Heavy? 770 to 948 pounds

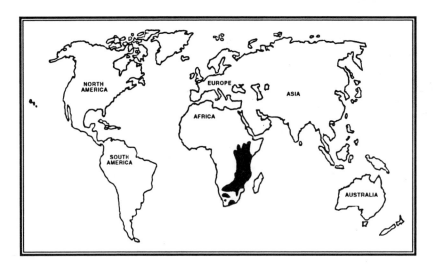

In Swahili, the zebra is called "punda milia," a name that means "striped donkey." But unlike donkeys, zebras have stubbornly resisted all of the African natives' attempts to tame them. Zebras are born to be wild.

There are three kinds of zebras. Burchell's zebra and Grevvy's zebra live in East Africa. The mountain zebra inhabits the mountainous regions at the southern tip of Africa. Burchell's zebra is a short-eared, stocky animal with bold body stripes and a pale rump. Grevvy's zebra is taller, with large, fringed ears and narrow stripes. The mountain zebra has thick black stripes on its rump.

Male zebras are called stallions, and each zebra band is led by a single dominant stallion. Young females stay with their mothers for about 15 months, while the young males may stay with mom for as long as three years.

Although their black and white colors seem loud and bold, the zebra's stripes really serve as camouflage. Zebras are hard for other animals to spot when they stand in the shade of trees or in the waves of hot air that rise from the African plains.

For safety, zebras mingle with herds of wildebeest, giraffes, antelopes, and other species. The animals cooperate by warning each other when predators are nearby. If a zebra is attacked and senses that it is going to die, it puts itself in a state of shock. In this condition, it no longer feels any pain from the attack.

ZEBRA ZONKERS

- Name the three kinds of zebras.
- What other animals do zebras like to mingle with?
- What does a zebra do when it's being attacked and knows it's going to die?
- How do you say "zebra" in Swahili?
- Would it be a good idea for you to have a pet zebra? Why or why not?

Where in the World Do They Live?

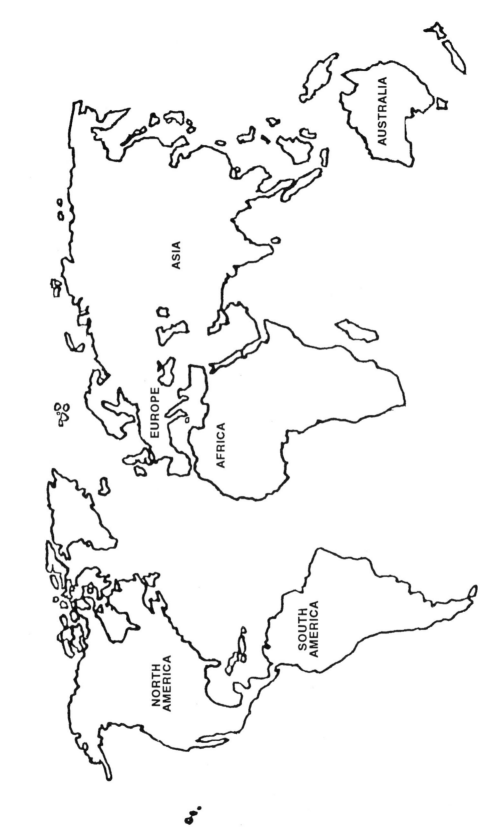

Look at the animals on the next page. Can you find the places on this map where each animal lives?

If you like to learn about animals, here are more animal books from NorthWord Press.

Moose for Kids
by Jeff Fair

Is a moose heavier than four refrigerators? What are antlers for, anyway? Find out in *Moose for Kids!*

Eagles for Kids
by Charlene Gieck

Bald eagles are the symbol of America. Pictures of these fierce birds plus eagle facts are in *Eagles for Kids!*

Whales for Kids
by Tom Wolpert

Deep in the ocean, these giants swim. Sometimes, though, they come up to say hello! See them in *Whales for Kids!*

Wolves for Kids
by Tom Wolpert

Should you be afraid of a big bad wolf? Probably not. *Wolves for Kids* tells you why.

Bears for Kids
by Jeff Fair

Crawl into the den with a bear and its cubs. Here's everything you wanted to know about black bears.

Whitetails for Kids
by Tom Wolpert

Where do deer live? How do they talk to each other? You'll find the facts and photos in *Whitetails for Kids*.

Published by NorthWord Press, Inc., P.O. Box 1360, Minocqua, WI 54548.
For a free catalog of nature books and gifts, call 1-800-336-5666.